VIRTUE STORIES
Play Fair

Lalita Iyer

Om
KIDZ

An imprint of Om Books International

Sharon hopped and skipped to the play area with her brand-new ball. As she entered, she noticed a group of kids. As soon as they saw her, they moved away.

'No one wants to play with me,' she wailed. 'No one wants to be my friend.'

Her brother Aron who was jumping on the trampoline, noticed her whining. 'Maybe because you don't play fair?' he said.

'What do you mean?' she asked.

'You are five. You should know,' he said, like a grown up. Sharon hated it when Aron acted all grown up although he was just three years older to her.

'Okay, come jump with me on the trampoline and I will explain,' he said. Each time you answer, you have to jump higher, okay?'

'Okay.'

'So, what do you do when you lose in a game?'

Sharon knew the answer and she was embarrassed. 'I cry,' she said and jumped.

'Is that all?'

'No wait, I insist on winning,' she said,
and jumped higher.
'I also feel sad when I lose. I hate losing.'

Aron rolled his eyes.

'Hmm, so what do you do when someone takes your teddy to play with it? '

'Well, I .... I scream and shout till she gives it back to me.' But her lips were quivering as she said it.

'You forgot to jump,' said Aron.

'Oh, yes.'

'Why does it make you mad when someone takes your things?'

'Because they are mine.
How dare they?' Even as she
said it, she felt horrible.

'What do you do when Manu comes
home and Mama asks you to give
him a turn at the computer when
you are playing a game?'

'I get mad... but I do it sulkily
because Mama said so,' she said.

'You forgot to jump.'

When Sharon jumped this time, something changed inside her. Another Sharon within her was saying, *you know, he is right!*

Soon it was time to go home. She
could hear her mother call, 'Sharon,
Aron, come home. Bath time.'

As they ran inside, Sharon said, 'I am going second.'

Aron said, 'No, you go first.'

'Why?' she asked.

'Because you are younger than me,' he laughed.

'Not fair,' said Sharon and they both laughed.